Trackers 0–5

Tracking children's progress through the Early Years Foundation Stage

by
Colin Gallow

A QEd Publication

Published in 2007

Many of the statements are taken from *The Early Years Foundation Stage* (DCFS, 2007).

ISBN 978 1 898873 51 8

British Library Cataloguing
A catalogue record for this book is available from the British Library.

Published by QEd Publications, 39 Weeping Cross, Stafford ST17 0DG
Tel: 01785 620364
Fax: 01785 607797
Website: www.qed.uk.com
Email: orders@qed.uk.com

Acknowledgements
Hannah Mortimer for her clear thinking and practical guidance.
Deborah Falshaw, Horn End Nursery; Marg Randles, Busy Bees Childcare; Samantha McIntosh, Caring Daycare Nurseries, Ann Ross for their valuable contributions. And the many others – childminders, early years advisers, and nursery staff who provided feedback.

Printed by Gutenberg Press Ltd, Malta.

Contents

Introduction

Guidance for parents and carers

Whatever setting your child is in, whether in a nursery or with a registered childminder, the overall aim will be to help your child:

- develop as a unique individual;
- form positive relationships with others;
- feel ready to develop, to play and to learn.

From September 2008 all early years providers have to meet certain standards set out in the Early Years Foundation Stage (EYFS). One of the requirements is that members of staff use ongoing observations to monitor how your child is developing and learning and use these to plan their play and learning. There are many different ways in which observations can be made. One method of keeping track of all these observations is to use the *Trackers 0–5* booklet.

The Trackers are divided into the Areas of Learning that fit in with the EYFS framework. They relate to children aged 0 to 5 and show all the many steps that young children pass through before they go to school and into the year in which they start.

The EYFS divides children's experiences into six Areas of Learning. Within these, there are also certain Early Learning Goals (shown by the symbol (G)) which most children will be expected to reach before the end of the year in which they reach their fifth birthday.

Trackers 0–5 are also useful for sharing valuable information with parents or carers, enabling you to keep in touch with your child's progress and allowing a much closer partnership with the setting. There is a general observation form at the end of each Area of Learning, and a comments box on most pages for you to add any comments you wish to make.

It is important to remember that each child is unique and no two will follow exactly the same pathway of development. Remember too that these early steps in playing and learning are very important if your child is going to be able to make good progress later on. Play is how young children learn and we should not rush them into more formal teaching and learning until they are ready. So please do not be concerned if there are gaps in your child's record. It might be that staff members have not yet had the opportunity to observe that area recently or that your child is busy making progress in other ways. Children do things at very different ages and stages.

Guidance for early years staff and childminders

The Early Years Foundation Stage

All early years practitioners are expected to plan and provide play opportunities which foster **a unique child**, **positive relationships**, **enabling environments** and **learning and development**. To help them achieve this, there are EYFS resources such as a CD-ROM, poster and Principle into Practice cards. There is also EYFS Practice Guidance which contains non-statutory guidance, additional advice and a set of Learning and development grids. These describe the steps that many children go through as they collect experiences and gather learning opportunities on their path towards the **Early Learning Goals**.

Keeping track

Many practitioners have found it helpful to have an individual progress record for each child in their care. This enables them to track progress, know at a glance how each child is playing and learning, and serve as the basis for forward planning and talking with parents and carers. *Trackers 0–5* serves this purpose and should be used alongside (rather than instead of) the ongoing observational assessment which informs your planning for each child's continuing development. It is important that *Trackers 0–5* are used flexibly since each child is unique and follows his or her own pathway of development.

Trackers 0–5 provide a method of tracking, or following, a child's development through the EYFS. They are not a curriculum in themselves; the framework you should be following is fully described in the Early Years Foundation Stage Statutory Framework and the Early Years Foundation Stage Practice Guidance.

Who the Trackers are for

These progress trackers will be useful for early years educators working in all kinds of early years settings: childminders, nursery classes, foundation classes, pre-schools, playgroups, private nurseries, day nurseries and creches. It will also be helpful for individuals training on NVQ or early childhood education courses and of interest to parents and carers of children who are interested in tracking and supporting their children's development through the EYFS.

The six Areas of Learning

These Trackers have been designed to be simple and usable, yet to link into the Government's *Early Years Foundation Stage* (Department for Children, Schools and Families, 2007). The guidance focuses on how children learn and what adults can do to encourage that learning. It identifies six Areas of early learning:

- Personal, Social and Emotional Development.

- Communication, Language and Literacy.

- Problem Solving, Reasoning and Numeracy.

- Knowledge and Understanding of the World.

- Physical Development.

- Creative Development.

Early Learning Goals

Within each Area of Learning, there are Early Learning Goals which most children will be expected to reach by the end of the year in which they reach their fifth birthday. Each page of the Trackers carries the title of one area of development within that particular Area of Learning, and weaves in some of the skills-based stages which users will already be familiar with and also builds in approximations to the Early Learning Goals given in the guidance (in some instances the exact wording has been used, in others the language has been changed for clarity or examples have been provided). For the full and accurate wording of the Early Learning Goals you will need to refer to the EYFS Practice Guidance.

Each Tracker contains between 14 and 30 statements of developmental stages, skills, understanding or competence, most of which can be easily observed or easily interpreted using the EYFS Practice Guidance. Some of these are taken from typical developmental stages that children pass through in their early years. Others relate to the Early Learning Goals. So that you can identify them easily, approximations to the Early Learning Goals are marked with this symbol (G) .

How to use the Trackers

Use one progress Tracker booklet for each child. Observe the child during your daily play and care activities and keep separate records of all your ongoing observations. If you feel that the child has reached that particular stage most of the time (we all have good days and bad days), you can record this in the Trackers, recording the date of your observation and the relevant information in the evidence column. Revisit the Trackers at regular intervals. You will then find that you are gradually able to observe and record more and more steps as the child develops and gathers experiences.

Examples

Some settings use a system in which a single tick indicates that a child sometimes manages a particular skill, and a double tick to indicate that the child has mastered that skill and can demonstrate it in different situations. Some use a circle that indicates a stage of learning and practising and a line through the circle to indicate that the child has mastered the skill.

An example of one system that seems to be widely used is shown below. Observations during each term are entered in a different colour with the first side of a triangle completed when you notice the child first performing that step, the second for when it is being practised, and the third for 'mastery'.

/ = first noticed	/\ = learning, practising	/\ = mastered

	Dates		Evidence
Use increasing mobility to connect with toys, objects and people	1/10/06 13/10/06 06/04/07	/\	Crawls to soft toys pile. Attempts to grasp teddy. Grasps small beanbag and throws it away. Grasps small ball and rolls it to Mum. Well directed too!
Operate equipment by means of pushing and pulling movements.	4/10/07	/	See observation sheet 8. Shows some interest in cooker controls.
Experiment with different ways of moving	16/11/07 20/11/07	/\	Watches other children dance to music. Joins in the sing and dance session – trying different actions.
Travel around, under, over and through balancing and climbing equipment (G)	20/12/07	/	With Sam's help, shows interest in trying climbing equipment.

Other settings prefer to adapt the recording column flexibly to suit their own recording system. The thing to do is choose a system to suit your setting and keep it simple.

There is a space at the bottom for your additional comments. For example, you might wish to record that a child was unwell for a while in order to explain why there was a setback in their confidence. You might add a comment that a child went into hospital for grommets on a certain date and that might explain why speech and understanding suddenly improved. Or you could add qualifying comments such as 'only if a familiar adult is present'.

Make sure that you have actual evidence for each of the items you record. Work on your actual observations rather than on hearsay. This is simply because you need to know which items still need encouragement or teaching and which are well established as part of the child's repertoire.

Planning the observations and providing evidence

Some settings find it easiest to delegate responsibility for the tracking to different members of staff. For example, each child should be assigned to one key person who could be responsible for tracking the development of a small group of children. Other settings might ascribe a certain Area of Learning to a particular member of staff who would also have the responsibility for planning and developing opportunities and activities in that area for that term.

Plan certain activities or opportunities which are going to allow you to observe a particular aspect of all the children's development that session, for example sand play with small and large buckets to encourage the understanding of size. Always aim for a balance between adult-led and child-initiated activity.

Make all observations in as natural a way as possible so that the children are not aware of a different situation or the fact that you are observing them.

Remember that *Trackers 0–5* form just one aspect of your ongoing observation and planning. You can collect a variety of observational evidence through sources such as children's work, photographs and parent/carer input. These will help you to track significant achievements in each child's learning and allow you to plan for their developmental needs.

Find regular opportunities to share progress with parents and carers. Compare notes and share successes.

Meeting individual needs

As part of your regular observation, you may notice that a particular child is developing rather patchily or following a different pathway. Perhaps there is one or more aspect of their development that is not progressing as fast as the others. This provides you with useful information for planning new learning opportunities for that child. Because the progress Trackers make you aware of the possible 'next steps' that each child passes through, you can play alongside the child to teach and encourage an appropriate next step. The Trackers are not set out rigorously in developmental sequence and each child will develop individually. However, there is an approximate progression from age nought to five with the youngest stages at the top of each page to the oldest stage at the bottom. Remember that each child is unique and follows his or her own pathway of development.

Sometimes you might be aware that a child has SEN because their development is significantly different from what you would normally expect for that age. You will also need to refer to *The Special Educational Needs Code of Practice* (DfES, 2001) for further guidance on meeting their needs or refer to *The SEN Code of Practice in Early Years Settings* published by QEd Publications. You will also find *Playladders* (Mortimer, 2000) a useful tool for observing and supporting children with special needs in your setting.

It is important that you *communicate* with parents or carers regarding the progress Trackers. Parents may be alarmed if they see that a large number of statements have not been 'ticked off' and may fear that their child is not progressing. These Trackers should not be seen as a definitive guide to a child's progress, they simply represent one further way of observing, recording and tracking progress. Sometimes parents may need reassuring that it is quite normal for children's development to progress at very different rates.

References

DfES (2001) *The Special Educational Needs Code of Practice*. Nottingham: DfES Publications.

DCFS (2007) *The Early Years Foundation Stage*. Nottingham: DCFS Publications.

Mortimer, H. (2000) *Playladders*. Stafford: QEd Publications.

Mortimer, H. (2002) *The SEN Code of Practice in Early Years Settings*. Stafford: QEd Publications.

Area of Learning

Personal, Social and Emotional Development

Aspects of Personal, Social and Emotional Development

- **Dispositions and Attitudes** – how children become interested, excited and motivated about their learning.

- **Self-confidence and Self-esteem** – about children having a sense of their own value and understanding the need for sensitivity to significant events in their own and other people's lives.

- **Making Relationships** – about the importance of children forming good relationships with others and working alongside others.

- **Behaviour and Self-control** – how children develop a growing understanding of what is right and wrong and why, together with learning about the impact of their words and actions on themselves and others.

- **Self-care** – how children gain a sense of self-respect and concern for their own personal hygiene and care and how they develop independence.

- **Sense of Community** – how children understand and respect their own needs, views, cultures and beliefs and those of other people.

From *The Early Years Foundation Stage* (DCFS, 2007)

Trackers 0–5

Area of Learning	Personal; Social and Emotional Development
Focus	Dispositions and Attitudes

/ = first noticed	∧ = learning, practising	△ = mastered

	Dates	Evidence
Enjoys looking at faces		
Play with own fists and feet		
Play peep bo games		
Put arms up to be lifted		
Watch other children when held close		
Shows when dislikes something		
Interested in new people and toys		
Repeat play sequences (e.g. putting in/emptying out)		
Willing to explore new activities with support		
Know who to go to for for help		
Know where to find toys		
Follow the routines of the session easily		
Willing to try new experiences		
Coping with changes in routine		
Call out to others to attract their attention		
Enjoy being with other children		
Repeat an action to get a response		

Trackers 0–5

Area of Learning	Personal, Social and Emotional Development
Focus	Dispositions and Attitudes

/ = first noticed	∧ = learning, practising	△ = mastered

	Dates	Evidence
Keen and interested in the activities		
Choose between activities		
Delight in own successes		
Know likes and dislikes		
Play happily in a large group		
Begin to settle for 5 to 10 minutes on an activity		
Become really involved when playing favourite activity		
Persist for a long time at a chosen activity		
Continue to be interested, excited and motivated to learn (G)		
Confident to speak in a familiar group (G)		
Confident to try new activities and initiate ideas (G)		
Pay attention and concentrate when need to (G)		
Sit quietly for appropriate activities (G)		

Comments

Trackers 0–5

Area of Learning	Personal, Social and Emotional Development
Focus	Self-confidence and Self-esteem

/ = first noticed	∧ = learning, practising	△ = mastered

	Dates	Evidence
Like to be looked at and approved of		
Comforted by touch and holding		
Enjoy snuggling in for comfort		
Separate from parent/carer with confidence		
Enjoy having approval		
Look happy and settled even when an adult is not nearby		
Share a laugh and a chuckle		
Enjoy the company of other children		
Able to make choices in play		
Can cope with new people/children/activities if a familiar person is nearby		
Can tell you which setting they go to, and talk about what they do there		
Able to set challenges in their play		
Asserts self if someone takes a toy he/she is playing with		
Recognise dangers and knows who to turn to for help		
Draw others' attention to something they are proud of		
Continue to feel content when not the centre of attention		

Trackers 0–5

Area of Learning	Personal, Social and Emotional Development
Focus	Self-confidence and Self-esteem

/ = first noticed	∧ = learning, practising	△ = mastered

	Dates	Evidence
Can handle changes in regular routine		
Talk freely about home and where he/she lives		
Willing and happy to play with children who are new to the setting		
Happy to talk and share ideas in a large group		
Let you know when feeling angry/anxious/sad in appropriate ways		
Let you know what his/her needs are, in appropriate ways		
Has an awareness and pride in self and recognises they are unique with abilities		
Respond to significant experiences, showing a range of feelings when appropriate (G)		
Becoming more sensitive to how others feel, think and what they need (G)		
Aware of what they feel, what they think and what they need (G)		
Has a developing respect for own culture and beliefs, and those of others (G)		

Comments

Trackers 0–5

Area of Learning	Personal, Social and Emotional Development
Focus	Making Relationships

/ = first noticed	∧ = learning, practising	△ = mastered

	Dates	Evidence
Enjoy being sociable		
Like to have a familiar adult nearby		
Call out for attention, comfort and play		
Pull or tug at adult to gain attention		
Start to play with other children		
Move close to others sometimes as he/she plays		
Show caring towards others		
Enjoy playing with an adult		
Happy to play alongside others		
Adapt how he/she behaves to fit in with others		
Form friendships		
Form good relationships with adults and other children (G)		
Work as part of a group or class (G)		
Take turns and share fairly (G)		
Understand that we need rules to help us work and play together (G)		

Comments

Trackers 0–5

Area of Learning	Personal, Social and Emotional Development
Focus	Behaviour and Self-control

/ = first noticed	∧ = learning, practising	△ = mastered

	Dates	Evidence
Soothed by warmth and comfort from others		
Follow simple routines and simple boundaries		
Know that some things are theirs and some things need to be shared		
Understand 'yes' and 'no'		
Aware that some things they do can hurt others		
Behave in a way that makes others feel happy/settled		
Show care and concern when others are upset		
Show care and concern for living creatures		
Aware that plants and trees need caring for		
Know when some wrong has been done to them and tells adult		
Tell you when they see others treated hurtfully		
Know what the rules and boundaries are and follows them most of the time		
Understand what is right and wrong and why (G)		
Consider the consequences of their words and actions for themselves and others (G)		

Comments

Trackers 0–5

Area of Learning	Personal, Social and Emotional Development
Focus	Self-care

/ = first noticed	∧ = learning, practising	△ = mastered

	Dates	Evidence
Look interested at food times		
Point to the foods or drinks they want		
Indicate that nappy needs changing		
Hold arms or legs up when being dressed		
Wants to try some things 'all by myself'		
Use the potty successfully with reminders		
Make a choice and stick by it		
Join in simple routines (e.g. moving the chairs)		
Fetch coat/apron at the right time		
Ask for help and guidance with confidence		
Undress self independently (G)		
Dress self independently (G)		
Manage own personal hygiene (G)		
Select play activities independently and find what is needed to enjoy that activity (G)		

Comments

Trackers 0–5

Area of Learning	Personal, Social and Emotional Development
Focus	Sense of Community

/ = first noticed	/\ = learning, practising	△ = mastered

	Dates	Evidence
Show different behaviours and reactions in different situations		
Pleased to be greeted when arriving		
Know that their voice/actions affects others		
Know that they are like others in certain ways		
Know that there are some things special to them		
Can tell you the names of four or five other children		
Can tell you which group they belong to		
Can tell you where they live		
Talks about home when they are in the setting		
Brings things from home to share or show		
Interested in the ways different people live		
Happy to talk about where they belong – 'my family, my group, my community'		
Understand that people have different needs, views, cultures and beliefs and respects this (G)		
Understand that they can expect others to treat them with respect (G)		

Comments

General Observation and Planning Form

Activity	Comment	Member of staff/ parent/carer	Date

Activity	Planning Changes	Member of staff/ parent/carer	Date

Area of Learning

Communication, Language and Literacy

Aspects of Communication, Language and Literacy

- **Language for Communication** – how children become communicators. Learning to listen and speak emerges out of non-verbal communication which includes facial expression, eye contact, and hand gesture. These skills develop as children interact with others, listen to and use language, extend their vocabulary and experience stories, songs, poems and rhymes.

- **Language for Thinking** – how children learn to use language to imagine and recreate roles and experiences . . . how they use talk to clarify their thinking and ideas or refer to events they have observed or are curious about.

- **Linking Sounds and Letters** – how children develop the ability to distinguish between sounds and become familiar with rhyme, rhythm and alliteration. They develop understanding of the correspondence between spoken and written sounds and learn to link sounds and letters and used their knowledge to read and write simple words by sounding out and blending.

- **Reading** – about children understanding and enjoying stories, books and rhymes, recognising that print carries meaning, both fiction and fact, and reading a range of familiar words and simple sentences.

- **Writing** – how children build an understanding of the relationship between the spoken and written word and how through making marks, drawing and personal writing children ascribe meaning to text and attempt to write for various purposes.

- **Handwriting** – the ways in which children's random marks, lines and drawings develop and form the basis of recognisable letters.

From *The Early Years Foundation Stage* (DCFS, 2007)

Trackers 0–5

Area of Learning	Communication, Language and Literacy
Focus	Language for Communication

/ = first noticed	∧ = learning, practising	△ = mastered

	Dates	Evidence
Make a range of sounds (crying, gurgling, babbling, squealing)		
Use early sounds and noises as signals for you to give attention		
Use one or two words consistently as labels (e.g. mama/dada)		
Make up some sounds/words to mean things		
Eager to use words to 'tell you' things		
Use single words to tell you what they want (e.g. 'di' for 'drink')		
Use two-word utterances (e.g. 'mama car')		
Respond to simple instructions		
Can use 10 clear words		
Ask simple questions		
Make simple statements/comments during play		
Listen to others in a small group		
Give simple explanations		
Use describing words (e.g. 'big') and possession words (e.g. 'mine')		
Follow simple direction words such as in/on/under		
Use intonation, rhythm and phrasing when talking to you		
Speak in more complex sentences		

Trackers 0–5

Area of Learning	Communication, Language and Literacy
Focus	Language for Communication

/ = first noticed	∧ = learning, practising	△ = mastered

	Dates	Evidence
Use 50 words to talk about things of interest		
Listen and respond to group instructions		
Stick more or less to the topic of conversation		
Retell a simple story		
Use language for increasing range of purposes (ask for information, to describe, remember and to explain)		
Talk with confidence to visitors		
Is aware of the listener's point of view (e.g. pauses to make sure you are listening)		
Make up stories, songs and rhymes		
Answer questions about a story		
Interact with others, negotiating plans and activities and taking turns in conversation (G)		
Use conventions such as 'please' and 'thank you' (G)		
Listen with sustained attention and join in with questions and comments (G)		
Extend vocabulary, exploring the meanings and sounds of new words (G)		
Show awareness of the listener when speaking (G)		
Speak clearly and audibly with confidence and control (G)		

Comments

Trackers 0–5

Area of Learning	Communication, Language and Literacy
Focus	Language for Thinking

/ = first noticed	/\ = learning, practising	△ = mastered

	Dates	Evidence
Use actions and sounds together to tell you what they need		
Respond to familiar requests in familiar contexts		
Use actions and words to comment on the 'here' and 'now'		
Use simple language and behaviour to tell others how they feel		
Use language with other children in order to sustain play		
Talk through what they are doing while playing		
Manage to control impulses some of the time by thinking before acting		
Talk through something that is going to happen to them in the near future		
Talk about something in the recent past		
Talk about a simple sequence (e.g. 'First we had tea, then we played outside')		
Link cause and effect and tell you what might happen next		
Talk about imaginary situations		
Use language to imagine and recreate roles and experiences (G)		
Use talk to organise, sequence and clarify thinking, ideas, feelings and events (G)		

Comments

Trackers 0–5

Area of Learning	Communication, Language and Literacy
Focus	Linking Sounds and Letters

/ = first noticed	∧ = learning, practising	△ = mastered

	Dates	Evidence
Watch your face and listen to your tone of voice with interest		
Repeat strings of sounds when babbling (e.g. 'ma – ma – ma')		
Make a range of speech sounds		
Join in a simple action rhyme		
Say one or two words with meaning		
Ask for toys with sounds as well as gestures		
Listen to and enjoy rhymes and songs		
Use six or more recognisable words		
Put two words together		
Speak in short phrases		
Use tone and rhythm to add meaning		
Know what a sound is even if it is out of sight (e.g. ambulance)		
Repeat words or phrases in familiar stories		
Can clap the rhythm of their name		
Clap a familiar rhythm (e.g. Hickory Dickory Dock)		
Can continue a rhyming string (e.g. when I was one I ate a ...)		

Trackers 0–5

Area of Learning	Communication, Language and Literacy
Focus	Linking Sounds and Letters

/ = first noticed	∧ = learning, practising	△ = mastered

		Dates	Evidence
Hear and say the first letter sound of their name			
Can listen to some letter sounds and point to the correct letter			
Can tell you the sound a word begins with when listening to simple words (e.g. <u>d</u>og)			
Repeat the first sound of a word (e.g. car starts with 'c')			
Make up words and sounds to go with their play			
Tell you words that rhyme with cat/toe/tree			
Can tell you the sound a word ends with when listening to simple words (e.g. ta<u>p</u>)			
Can repeat the short vowel sound in a word when listening to simple words (e.g. c<u>a</u>t)			
Blend letters to read CVC words and recognise common digraphs (e.g. 'br' 'sh')			
Hear and say sounds in words in the order in which they occur	Ⓖ		
Link sounds to letters, naming and sounding the letters of the alphabet	Ⓖ		
Use phonic knowledge to write simple, regular words (e.g. c – a – t)	Ⓖ		
Make phonetically plausible attempts at more complex words	Ⓖ		

Comments

Trackers 0–5

Area of Learning	Communication, Language and Literacy
Focus	Reading

/ = first noticed	∧ = learning, practising	△ = mastered

	Dates	Evidence
Enjoy finger rhymes		
Handle and explore a soft cover book		
Enjoy looking at pictures		
Respond to interactive games such as 'clap hands'		
Hold and look at a picture book, attempting to turn pages		
Look at photographs with interest		
Hold picture book correctly and help you turn pages		
Fetch a picture book to share with you		
Begin to make links between a picture book and their surroundings		
Listen to and join in with stories in a small group		
Suggest what might happen next in a story		
Share a picture book with another child		
Pretend to read a familiar picture book, remembering the broad details		
'Read' an unfamiliar picture book by making up a story based on the pictures		
Select a card with their name on		
Show an interest in print in the environment		
Know what some familiar signs say or mean		

Trackers 0–5

Area of Learning	Communication, Language and Literacy
Focus	Reading

/ = first noticed	∧ = learning, practising	△ = mastered

	Dates	Evidence
Begin to recognise some familiar words		
Enjoy an increasing range of books		
Know that information can be retrieved from books and computers		
Use their phonic knowledge to read simple regular words and make phonetically plausible attempts at longer or more complex words		
Show an understanding of the elements of stories – can tell you what happened at the beginning, middle and end		
Explore and experiment with sounds, words and texts (G)		
Retell narratives in the correct sequence, drawing on language patterns of stories (G)		
Read a range of familiar and common words and simple sentences independently (G)		
Know that print carries meaning and, in English, is read from left to right and top to bottom (G)		
Show an understanding of the elements of stories such as main character, sequence of events and openings (G)		
Know how information can be found in non-fiction books to answer questions about where, who, why and how (G)		

Comments

Trackers 0–5

Area of Learning	Communication, Language and Literacy
Focus	Writing
/ = first noticed	∧ = learning, practising △ = mastered

	Dates	Evidence
Enjoy dabbling hands in water		
Play with liquids on surfaces, e.g. puddles on the table		
Begin to make marks by dabbing or smearing		
Examine marks they make and those of others		
Repeat marks (e.g. strokes or rounds)		
Sometimes tell you that their marks mean words		
Pretend to 'write'		
Know that some marks have meanings (e.g. what familiar logos mean, such as a favourite food chain)		
Dictate a simple phrase to you, breaking speech into separate words		
Use writing to record things and communicate with		
Use their phonic knowledge to write simple, regular words and make phonetically plausible attempts at more complex words (G)		
Attempt writing for different purposes, using features of different forms such as lists, stories and instructions (G)		
Write own name and other things such as labels and captions (G)		
Begin to form simple sentences, sometimes using punctuation (G)		

Comments

Trackers 0–5

Area of Learning	Communication, Language and Literacy
Focus	Handwriting

/ = first noticed	∧ = learning, practising	△ = mastered

	Dates	Evidence
Play with their fingers and toes		
Study fingers carefully as they repeat patterns of movement		
Reach for an object and secure it with their fingers		
Use a poking movement in their play		
Hold small toys and strings		
Hold chunky crayons and scribble freely		
Paint and dab with better control		
Make large circular movement when painting		
Copy a vertical and horizontal line		
Begin to make anticlockwise movements to make letter-like shapes		
Write the first letter of their name		
Form a few recognisable letters		
Use a pencil and hold it effectively ⓖ		
Use a pencil to form recognisable letters, most of which are correctly formed ⓖ		

Comments

General Observation and Planning Form

Activity	Comment	Member of staff/ parent/carer	Date

Activity	Planning Changes	Member of staff/ parent/carer	Date

Area of Learning

Problem Solving, Reasoning and Numeracy

Aspects of Problem Solving, Reasoning and Numeracy

- **Numbers as Labels and for Counting** – how children gradually know and use numbers and counting in play, and eventually recognise and use numbers reliably, to develop mathematical ideas and to solve problems.

- **Calculating** – how children develop an awareness of the relationship between numbers and amounts and know that numbers can be combined to be 'added together' and can be separated by 'taking away' and that two or more amounts can be compared.

- **Shape, Space and Measures** – how through talking about shapes and quantities, and developing appropriate vocabulary, children use their knowledge to develop ideas and to solve mathematical problems.

From *The Early Years Foundation Stage* (DCFS, 2007)

Trackers 0–5

Area of Learning	Problem Solving, Reasoning and Numeracy
Focus	Numbers as Labels and for Counting

/ = first noticed	∧ = learning, practising	△ = mastered

	Dates	Evidence
Notices changes in how things are arranged around them		
Enjoy number rhymes and naming games (e.g. eyes, nose and tummy)		
Use some counting words randomly while playing		
Know when things belong to someone (e.g. 'Daddy's')		
Show curiosity in number symbols		
Experiment with symbols and marks		
Use 'more' or 'lots' or 'all gone' in play		
Recite some number names in sequence		
Interested in the number relating to their age		
Identify numerals '1', '2' or '3' when asked		
Join in simple number rhymes		
Match number and quantity		
Recognise groups with 1, 2 or 3 objects		
Begin to represent numbers by holding up correct number of fingers		
Select numeral to represent 1 to 5 objects		
Arrange numerals 1 to 9 in correct sequence		
Select correct numeral to represent 1 to 9 objects		

Trackers 0–5

Area of Learning	Problem Solving, Reasoning and Numeracy
Focus	Numbers as Labels and for Counting

/ = first noticed	∧ = learning, practising	△ = mastered

	Dates	Evidence
Know that numbers identify how many objects are in a set		
Use ordinal numbers in different contexts (e.g. first, second)		
Count out 5 objects with one-to-one correspondence		
Begin to count beyond 10		
Estimate how many objects they can see and check by counting		
Count aloud in ones, twos, fives or tens		
Match then compare the number of objects in two sets		
Use language such as 'more' or 'less' to compare two numbers		
Say and use number names in order in familiar contexts (G)		
Count reliably up to 10 everyday objects (G)		
Recognise numerals 1 to 9 (G)		
Use developing mathematical ideas and methods to solve practical problems (G)		

Comments

Trackers 0–5

Area of Learning	Problem Solving, Reasoning and Numeracy
Focus	Calculating

/ = first noticed	/\ = learning, practising	△ = mastered

	Dates	Evidence
Enjoy 'peek-a-boo' games		
Know that when you 'disappear' behind a screen you are still there		
Fill and empty containers		
Begin to classify (e.g. line up cars together)		
Match objects by colour		
Order two objects by height		
Order three objects by length		
Can give you the 'big' one		
Show an interest when you count steps		
Predict what number comes next in a familiar number rhyme (e.g. 'One, two, buckle my shoe ...')		
Continue a given pattern with blocks/beads (e.g. red–yellow–red–yellow– ...)		
Sort objects into sets when playing (e.g. people and cars)		
Begin to compare quantities in two sets		
Use numbers in talk (e.g. 'Danny has three')		
Know that one set becomes 'more' or 'less' if you add or take away things		

Trackers 0–5

Area of Learning	Problem Solving, Reasoning and Numeracy
Focus	Calculating

/ = first noticed	∧ = learning, practising	△ = mastered

	Dates	Evidence
Can tell you if two sets have the 'same number' (1 to 5)		
Order three objects by weight/capacity		
Use reasoning for solving practical problems (e.g. 'If I have three cups, I need three saucers')		
Find the total number by adding two sets (2 to 5)		
Use own methods to sort out a simple number problem		
Share objects into equal groups		
In practical activities and discussion, begin to use the vocabulary involved in adding and subtracting (G)		
Use language such as 'more' or 'less' to compare two numbers (G)		
Find one more or one less than a number from 1 to 10 (G)		
Begin to relate addition to combining two groups of objects and subtraction to 'taking away' (G)		

Comments

Trackers 0–5

Area of Learning	Problem Solving, Reasoning and Numeracy
Focus	Shape, Space and Measures

/ = first noticed	∧ = learning, practising	△ = mastered

	Dates	Evidence
Watch a mobile as it twists and turns		
Show interest in and stare at shapes (e.g. in a shape mobile)		
Explore shapes and solids using touch and mouthing		
Crawl into their own space on the floor		
Enjoy playing with covers and blankets		
Show interest in handling and exploring solid shapes		
Repeat movements in front of a mirror		
Arrange toys in spaces around them		
Fit a shape into a posting box toy		
Fit a shape into an inset board		
Enjoy pouring water between big and little containers and use this in simple problem solving		
Notice simple shapes and patterns in pictures		
Play successfully with shape posting toys		
Begin to understand variations in size		
Enjoy simple inset boards and jigsaws		
Recognise big things and small things in meaningful contexts		
Can show you which object is 'bigger than' or 'smaller than' another		

Trackers 0–5

Area of Learning	Problem Solving, Reasoning and Numeracy
Focus	Shape, Space and Measures

/ = first noticed	∧ = learning, practising	△ = mastered

	Dates	Evidence
Sort and match simple shapes		
Follow simple directional cues (e.g. 'up' and 'down')		
Use blocks in simple construction play		
Notice patterns around them and recreate these in their play or drawings		
Talk about the shapes of everyday objects		
Begin to use the names for 'solid' 3D shapes and 'flat' 2D shapes		
Work out which shape is needed to fit which space (e.g. in collage or designing)		
Enjoy playing with tunnels and bridges, using positional language like 'over' and 'under'		
Follow simple directions such as 'here', 'there', 'on top' and 'through'		
Grade a set of objects by size		
Order two items by length or height		
Measure a length by pacing it out		
Order a group of children by height		
Enjoy using shapes in collage and talk about what they are doing		
Show an understanding of spaces in their small world and imaginative play		
Recognise and create symmetry in their play, patterns and artwork		

Trackers 0–5

Area of Learning	Problem Solving, Reasoning and Numeracy
Focus	Shape, Space and Measures

/ = first noticed	∧ = learning, practising	△ = mastered

		Dates	Evidence
Use a simple sand-timer to measure turn-taking			
Use everyday language related to time			
Know the sequence of events during a routine session			
Use language such as 'greater', 'smaller', 'heavier' or 'lighter' to compare quantities	Ⓖ		
Talk about, recognise and recreate simple patterns (why shapes are the same or different)	Ⓖ		
Use language such as 'circle' or 'bigger' to describe the shape of solids and flat shapes	Ⓖ		
Use everyday words to describe position	Ⓖ		
Use developing mathematical ideas and methods to solve practical problems	Ⓖ		

Comments

General Observation and Planning Form

Activity	Comment	Member of staff/ parent/carer	Date

Activity	Planning Changes	Member of staff/ parent/carer	Date

Area of Learning

Knowledge and Understanding of the World

Aspects of Knowledge and Understanding of the World

- **Exploration and Investigation** – how children investigate objects and materials and their properties, learn about change and patterns, similarities and differences, and question how and why things work.

- **Designing and Making** – ways in which children learn about the construction process, and tools and techniques that can be used to assemble materials creatively and safely.

- **ICT** – how children find out about and learn how to use appropriate information technology such as computers and programmable toys that support their learning.

- **Time** – how children find out about past and present events relevant to their own lives or those of their families.

- **Place** – how children become aware of and interested in the natural world, and find out about their local area, knowing what they like and dislike about it.

- **Communities** – how children begin to know about their own and other people's cultures in order to understand and celebrate the similarities and differences between them in a diverse society.

From *The Early Years Foundation Stage* (DCFS, 2007)

Trackers 0–5

Area of Learning	Knowledge and Understanding of the World
Focus	Exploration and Investigation

/ = first noticed	/\ = learning, practising	△ = mastered

	Dates	Evidence
Use early movements and senses to focus on and reach for objects		
Enjoy objects and playthings through shaking, banging and mouthing		
Pull self along the furniture to reach new objects of interest		
Explore and investigate playthings by putting in and emptying out		
Explore and play, looking for new experiences		
Ask others why things happen		
Begin to suggest why things happen		
Show curiosity and interest in living things		
Describe and talk about what they see and hear		
Interact with things in order to work out what they do and how they work		
Ask 'what' and 'why' questions, showing an awareness of change		
Interested in new activities and keen to experience and explore them		
Make links between their talking, doing and finding out through books or ICT		
Investigate objects and materials by using all of their senses as appropriate (G)		
Find out about, and identify some features of living things, objects and events they observe (G)		
Look closely at similarities, differences, patterns and change (G)		
Ask questions about why things happen and how things work (G)		

Trackers 0–5

Area of Learning	Knowledge and Understanding of the World
Focus	Designing and Making

/ = first noticed	∧ = learning, practising	△ = mastered

	Dates	Evidence
Explore objects using hands and mouth		
Enjoy watching when you stack bricks and knock them down		
Curious about containers that open and close		
Look inside a simple container in order to find the contents		
Play with push-along toys		
Walk pulling a wheeled toy on a cord		
Build a tower of 3 to 5 bricks		
Join construction pieces together		
Sustain play with blocks and construction pieces		
Use simple tools with play dough (e.g. to make holes, shapes etc)		
Use simple tools with supervision and support		
Construct with a set purpose in mind, using a variety of resources		
Use simple tools and techniques competently and appropriately		
Build and construct with a wide range of objects, selecting appropriate resources and adapting work where necessary (G)		
Select the tools and techniques needed to shape, assemble and join materials they are working with (G)		

Comments

Trackers 0–5

Area of Learning	Knowledge and Understanding of the World
Focus	ICT

/ = first noticed	∧ = learning, practising	△ = mastered

	Dates	Evidence
Interested in telephones and computer/TV screens		
Interested in buttons, knobs and dials on activity centre toys		
Enjoy lift-the-flap books		
Pretend to use the phone or simple camera		
Know what simple ICT equipment can do		
Interested and curious about ICT		
Operate a simple touch pad or switch		
Know how to operate simple equipment (e.g. turning a knob)		
Can select and take a photograph		
Begin to use a computer mouse, linking cause with effect		
Concentrate on and use a simple program on a computer		
Use ICT to perform simple functions (e.g. using a remote control)		
Find out about and identify the use of everyday technology (G)		
Use information and communication technology and programmable toys to support their learning (G)		

Comments

Trackers 0–5

Area of Learning	Knowledge and Understanding of the World
Focus	Time

/ = first noticed	/\ = learning, practising	△ = mastered

	Dates	Evidence
Anticipate what is about to happen (e.g. repeated sounds, sights or actions)		
Familiar with the regular routine		
Anticipate and cooperate at mealtimes and changing times		
Join in familiar routines such as putting a coat on to go outside		
Show through role-play that they can follow simple routines and sequences		
Recognise some special times in their life		
Share special times in others' lives		
Arrange photographs of a simple sequence of actions in order (e.g. getting up in the morning)		
Remember what they did previously and talk about past experiences		
Tell you about things they remember from before		
Talk about photographs of when they were younger		
Can begin to talk to you about what happened in their past and what is present		
Use words related to time in conversation		
Understand about the changing seasons of the year		
Make plans for the near future		
Find out about past and present events in their own life (G)		
Find out about past and present events in their family's lives and other people they know (G)		

Trackers 0–5

Area of Learning	Knowledge and Understanding of the World
Focus	Place

/ = first noticed	∧ = learning, practising	△ = mastered

	Dates	Evidence
Move arms and legs around to explore the place around them		
Creep, roll or crawl into new places		
Enjoy the outside and all that can be seen and heard there		
Enjoy watching animals and pets, commenting with words and actions		
Curious about their environment		
Enjoy small-world play such as farms and garages		
Able to extend small-world play by adding new ideas		
Interested to explore more about the world through books or ICT		
Ask questions about what is going on around them		
Talk about other places not in the 'here and now' such as their home or holiday		
Able to recreate features of the built environment in their models or art		
Notice differences between features of the local environment		
Observe, find out about and identify features in the place they live and the natural world (G)		
Find out about their environment, and talk about those features they like and dislike (G)		

Comments

Trackers 0–5

Area of Learning	Knowledge and Understanding of the World
Focus	Communities

/ = first noticed	∧ = learning, practising	△ = mastered

	Dates	Evidence
Focus intently on the faces around them		
Show pleasure in being amongst others		
Recognise familiar and special people (e.g. family, friends, key person)		
Show interest in the social life around them		
Enjoy looking at a photograph album of self and their family		
Know the names of many children in the setting		
Interested to hear about other children's lives and news		
Express their feelings about a significant personal event		
Tell parents or carers about what they have done in the group		
Talk about significant events at home to members of the group (e.g. a wedding, birthday)		
Talk about where they live and their local community		
Have an awareness of and talk about similarities and differences in others		
Have an awareness of the cultures and beliefs of others		
Begin to know about their own culture and beliefs and those of others (G)		

Comments

General Observation and Planning Form

Activity	Comment	Member of staff/ parent/carer	Date

Activity	Planning Changes	Member of staff/ parent/carer	Date

Area of Learning

Physical Development

Aspects of Physical Development

- **Movement and Space** – how children learn to move with confidence, imagination and safety, with an awareness of space, themselves and others.

- **Health and Bodily Awareness** – how children learn the importance of keeping healthy and the factors that contribute to maintaining their health.

- **Using Equipment and Materials** – ways in which children use a range of small and large equipment.

From *The Early Years Foundation Stage* (DCFS, 2007)

Trackers 0–5

Area of Learning	Physical Development
Focus	Movement and Space

/ = first noticed	∧ = learning, practising	△ = mastered

	Dates	Evidence
Arm and leg movements becoming more controlled		
Use arms and legs to make contact with things around them		
Watch movement of own hand in front of face		
Able to move away from the position they are placed in		
Kick and wave arms to music		
Crawl over rugs and cushions		
Love to creep, crawl or shuffle		
Creep or crawl towards something of interest		
Pick up a small toy		
Enjoy holding on to a hand or piece of furniture and 'bouncing'		
Toddle from one person to another (5 – 6 steps)		
Toddle at speed, using voice while moving		
Roll a ball between an adult and self		
Walk across the room		
Respond to sound with body movements		
Walk backwards		
Begin to show increasing control (e.g. jump, kick a ball, balance briefly on one leg)		

Trackers 0–5

Area of Learning	Physical Development
Focus	Movement and Space

/ = first noticed	∧ = learning, practising	△ = mastered

	Dates	Evidence
Avoid bumping into/treading over others		
Find own space on a crowded floor		
Run fast		
Move freely and confidently (e.g. rolling, running, jumping, hopping)		
Perform a range of movements imaginatively (e.g. squirming, twisting, walking on tiptoe)		
Run and change direction to avoid obstacles		
Show balance when playing (e.g. creeping, tiptoeing, bunny hopping)		
Throw a ball with approximate aim		
Begin to operate equipment (e.g. a computer mouse with a simple game)		
Climb up steps to slide or onto climbing frame		
Attempt range of movements on a climbing frame (e.g. climbing around, under, over, through)		
Make repeated attempts at a new skill		
Accept simple rules in a game of 'catch me' or ball kicking		
Move backwards and sideways as well as forwards		
March to a steady rhythm		
Try new ideas for moving (e.g. when dancing)		
Jump from a step and land safely		

Trackers 0–5

Area of Learning	Physical Development
Focus	Movement and Space

/ = first noticed	∧ = learning, practising	△ = mastered

	Dates	Evidence
Show awareness of the need for safety (e.g. walks carefully when carrying scissors)		
Manage own buttons and zips		
Thread large beads and stack small blocks		
Show preference for one hand consistently		
Handle construction materials with increasing control (cartons, planks, interlocking bricks)		
Move with confidence, imagination and in safety (G)		
Move with control and coordination (G)		
Show awareness of space, of self and of others (G)		
Travel around, under, over and through balancing and climbing equipment (G)		

Comments

Trackers 0–5

Area of Learning	Physical Development
Focus	Health and Bodily Awareness

/ = first noticed	∧ = learning, practising	△ = mastered

	Dates	Evidence
Thrive on positive care, attention and physical contact		
Let you know when they need a rest		
Show some awareness of bladder and bowel urges		
Indicate choice at meal and snack times		
Let you know when they need something (e.g.nappy needs changing, need a drink)		
Sometimes able to use a potty/toilet with reminders		
Dry by day		
Able to control bowels		
Feed self with a spoon and fork		
Show awareness of own needs (e.g. needing a tissue to wipe nose)		
Ask for drinks and food when they need them		
Can tell you what happens to their body after they have been running		
Wash hands after using the toilet		
Can tell you why they need a good sleep at night		
Show an awareness of good habits (e.g. washing hands before eating, throwing away used tissues)		
Recognise the importance of keeping healthy, and those things that contribute to this ⓖ		
Recognise the changes that happen to their bodies when they are active ⓖ		

Trackers 0–5

Area of Learning	Physical Development
Focus	Using Equipment and Materials

/ = first noticed	∧ = learning, practising	△ = mastered

	Dates	Evidence
Watch and explore hands and feet		
Touch and begin to hold objects		
Pass a small toy from one hand to another		
Imitate simple actions like clapping hands		
Use a pointing finger to indicate things		
Play putting in and emptying out of containers		
Poke with one finger		
Pummel and squash play dough		
Make marks in damp sand, paste or paint		
Roll out malleable materials		
Poke and make marks in wet sand with a simple tool		
Turn a simple dial/screwtop		
Balance blocks to create simple structures		
Use molds and templates to form and shape materials		
Show increasing control (e.g.operate a hammer and peg toy)		
Push and pull wheeled toys		
Use one-handled tools and equipment		

Trackers 0–5

Area of Learning	Physical Development
Focus	Using Equipment and Materials

/ = first noticed	⋀ = learning, practising	△ = mastered

	Dates	Evidence
Swing, slide and climb safely		
Enjoy small world play in wet or dry sand with increasing control and detail		
Understand the need for safety (e.g. know that spills need cleaning up)		
Explore malleable materials by squeezing, pinching, twisting and shaping		
Retrieve, collect and catch a selection of balls		
Manipulate materials to achieve a planned effect		
Use simple tools to effect changes in materials (e.g. use a hammer safely when woodworking)		
Explain why we need to handle tools safely		
Practise some appropriate safety measures even if not supervised		
Use a range of small and large equipment (G)		
Handle tools and objects safely and with increasing control (G)		
Handle construction and malleable materials safely and with increasing control (G)		

Comments

General Observation and Planning Form

Activity	Comment	Member of staff/ parent/carer	Date

Activity	Planning Changes	Member of staff/ parent/carer	Date

Area of Learning

Creative Development

Aspects of Creative Development

- **Being Creative – Responding to Experiences, Expressing and Communicating Ideas** – how children respond in a variety of ways to what they see, hear, smell, touch or feel and how, as a result of these encounters, they express and communicate their own ideas, thoughts and feelings.

- **Exploring Media and Materials** – finding out about, thinking about and working with colour, texture, shape, space and form in two and three dimensions.

- **Creating Music and Dance** – how sounds can be made and changed and how sounds can be recognised and repeated from a pattern . . . ways of exploring movement, matching movements to music and singing simple songs from memory.

- **Developing Imagination and Imaginative Play** – how children are supported to develop and build their imaginations through stories, role-play, imaginative play, dance, music, design and art.

From *The Early Years Foundation Stage* (DCFS, 2007)

Trackers 0–5

Area of Learning	Creative Development
Focus	Being Creative – Responding to Experiences, Expressing & Communicating Ideas

/ = first noticed	∧ = learning, practising	△ = mastered

	Dates	Evidence
Accompany movements with voice and sound		
Use a range of methods to communicate how they are feeling		
Respond to what they see		
Respond to what they hear		
Respond to what they feel and touch		
Respond to what they taste and smell		
Quieten and can focus when listening carefully		
Repeat patterns of play over and over		
Repeat actions in order to explore what effect something has		
Happy to explore an activity or object with someone else		
Call out for someone to look at something they have seen		
Look up at you as they play or create something		
Show you what they have done		
Seek to make sense of what they see, hear, touch, feel or smell		
Keen to share what they have created with other children		
Begin to use representation to communicate what they feel (e.g. jumping for excitement)		
Use talk to indicate personal satisfaction or frustration		

Trackers 0–5

Area of Learning	Creative Development
Focus	Being Creative – Responding to Experiences, Expressing & Communicating Ideas

/ = first noticed	∧ = learning, practising	△ = mastered

	Dates	Evidence
Tell you how they feel about their creation		
Show you how they feel through art and craft		
Show you how they feel through movement and dance		
Show a preference about how they like to express themselves (e.g. voice/music/dance/art)		
Talk about what they are trying to do in their creations and designs		
Respond to comments and questions about their creations		
Make comparisons and create new connections (e.g. make a connection between fireworks and being cold)		
Respond in a variety of ways to what they see, hear, touch and feel (G)		
Express and communicate their ideas, thoughts and feelings by using a widening range of materials, suitable tools, designing and making (G)		
Express and communicate their ideas, thoughts and feelings by using role-play, movement and a variety of songs and musical instruments (G)		

Comments

Trackers 0–5

Area of Learning	Creative Development
Focus	Exploring Media and Materials
/ = first noticed	⋀ = learning, practising △ = mastered

	Dates	Evidence
Enjoy watching colours or lights		
Enjoy crumpling and tearing paper		
Enjoy handling collage material		
Show early mark-making when playing with food and spills		
Explore and experiment media using their whole body (e.g. playing with paint, dough, bubbles)		
Dab with a glue stick		
Create simple patterns and structures using blocks		
Arrange and rearrange their food and playthings		
Enjoy finger painting and hand prints		
Begin to apply colours or paints to different surfaces		
Enjoy painting with a brush		
Snip with scissors		
Show interest in different textures (e.g. smooth, shiny, soft, hard surfaces)		
Explore colour and begin to match and sort by colour		
Explore lines and shapes		
Begin to construct 3D shapes, making enclosures and spaces		

Trackers 0–5

Area of Learning	Creative Development
Focus	Exploring Media and Materials

/ = first noticed	∧ = learning, practising	△ = mastered

	Dates	Evidence
Plan a creation ahead (e.g. 'I want to make a shiny, blue sea picture')		
Try different media to create new effects (e.g. a collage using paper, sand, fabric, pasta)		
Experiment to create different textures (e.g. puts glue on sawdust)		
Create paintings and drawings		
Plan a construction ahead (e.g. 'I want to build a castle so I'll need ...')		
Express their feelings using designing and making (e.g. 'I like this because ...')		
Select the best materials for the job (e.g. to make a strong bridge)		
Create constructions and collages		
Use ideas involving fitting, overlapping, in and out in their 3D creations		
Use ideas involving stripes, enclosures, grids and sunbursts in their representation		
Work creatively on a large or small scale		
Explore colour, texture, shape, form and space in two or three dimensions (G)		

Comments

Trackers 0–5

Area of Learning	Creative Development
Focus	Creating Music and Dance

/ = first noticed	∧ = learning, practising	△ = mastered

	Dates	Evidence
'Stills' to the sound of music		
Respond to familiar sounds (e.g. a voice)		
Enjoy a one-two rocking rhythm		
Move arms and legs vigorously to lively music		
Explore objects by banging		
Make noises to music		
Rattle a shaker when music is played		
Listen to and sometimes join in rhymes and familiar songs		
Join in with some words and actions when favourite songs are sung		
'Dance' to music (not yet to a beat)		
Create sounds by shaking, banging, tapping things		
Show an interest in the way musical instruments sound		
Join in with dancing and singing games		
Sing a few familiar songs, sometimes making up songs		
Tap out a simple beat with a percussion instrument		
Recognise and explore how sounds can be changed (e.g. playing loudly or softly)		

Trackers 0–5

Area of Learning	Creative Development
Focus	Creating Music and Dance

/ = first noticed	∧ = learning, practising	△ = mastered

	Dates	Evidence
Make up new ways of moving and dancing to music		
Can remember a range of dances and songs		
Explore the different sounds instruments make		
March or dance to a simple beat		
Dance confidently and freely		
Play loudly/softly in imitation		
Play quickly/slowly in imitation		
Sing and carry out actions at the same time (e.g. joining in 'Wheels on the bus' with words and actions)		
Recognise and explore how sounds can be changed (G)		
Sing simple songs from memory (G)		
Recognise repeated sounds and sound patterns (G)		
Match movements to music (G)		

Comments

Trackers 0–5

Area of Learning	Creative Development
Focus	Developing Imagination and Imaginative Play

/ = first noticed	⋀ = learning, practising	△ = mastered

	Dates	Evidence
Smile with pleasure at recognisable playthings		
Enjoy making noises and movements when encouraged		
Copy facial expressions (e.g. looks serious when adult does)		
Pretend one thing is something else (e.g. 'This box is teddy's bed')		
Pretend to be asleep		
Pretend one thing is something else, even if dissimilar (e.g. 'This brush is my horse')		
Act out pretend scenarios (e.g. have a tea party with the teddies)		
Copy adults doing something in their play		
Use available resources to create props to support their role-play		
Enjoy role-play (e.g. in a themed area)		
Engage in imaginative play, based on actual experiences		
Introduce a storyline into their play		
Play alongside children engaged in the same theme		
Play cooperatively in a group to act out a narrative or imaginative game		
Use their imagination in art and design, music and dance (G)		
Use their imagination in imaginative and role-play and stories (G)		

General Observation and Planning Form

Activity	Comment	Member of staff/ parent/carer	Date

Activity	Planning Changes	Member of staff/ parent/carer	Date

Contacts with external agencies	Date
(e.g. SENCO, school, GP, educational psychologist)	